MORBID
OBSESSIONS

Published in 2022 by Cipher Press
Ink Court
419 Wick Lane
London, E3 2PX

Paperback ISBN: 978-1-7397849-5-9

Interview with Natalia Santana Mendes printed with the permission of Heston Michaels (English Collective of Prostitutes) and Marina Oliveira Santos.

Printed and bound in the UK by TJ International
Distributed by Turnaround Publisher Services
Cover Design by Wolf Murphy-Merrydew
Typeset by Laura Jones

All proceeds after production costs from the sale of this book will be donated to Babeworld, a collective that seeks to create a more representative art world through the creation of art, fundraising, grants, and facilitation of events for those who are marginalised in the arts.

www.cipherpress.co.uk

MORBID
OBSESSIONS

On trans and sex worker bodies
and writing fiction from the margins

FRANKIE MIREN
& ALISON RUMFITT

INTRODUCTION BY
MORGAN M PAGE

Featuring an interview with
Natalia Santana Mendes

Cipher
press

INTRODUCTION

MORGAN M. PAGE

There's a war on, but only some of us know it's happening. Every day we watch all the little gay people and hookers in our phones rise and fall against the torrent of ever-more bizarre attempts to blame us for all of society's malaise. Today an American school shooting was blamed on a random trans teenager several states away by far-right pundits. Last week, a group of leftist women's organisations in the UK called for a ban on journalists using the words "sex worker" and "porn actress," conveniently while a so-called Online Safety Bill that would shutter many workers' only safe avenues of finding clients worked its way through UK Parliament. And yet, when I look up from my phone, walk around outside, eat dumplings in a lush but cheap restaurant by Victoria Park, I find myself having to sketch out the existence of this war to people again and again who seem to have never even heard of it.

It's not that people simply don't care what happens to trans people, to sex workers, to any of the other tabloid villains who become the target of these daily skirmishes (migrants, Black youth, Romani travellers, those who cannot afford skyrocketing energy bills, Channel 4). But it begins to feel as though we're living in parallel dimensions, whose harshest edges only occasionally rub up against each other and leave an impression.

Frankie Miren and Alison Rumitt are writing from the trenches. Their startling debuts *The Service* and *Tell Me I'm Worthless* have positioned them on the frontlines not only of underground British literature but of the very culture war itself. While in their novels, each has given us an unflinching portrait of contemporary TERF (trans exclusionary radical feminist) and SWERF (sex worker exclusionary radical feminist) politics, the stories in this collection take us down an ever darker path. Here we are invited into the minds of those sex workers and trans people who've become tangled up within the very same radicalising mechanisms that have so twisted the minds of our would-be exterminators.

Twitter and Mumsnet are the twin sleep paralysis demons camped out on our collective chest. A corrupting, viscous fluid leaks from their hungry jaws down into our prone eyes and ears that carries their disease, the chattering madness that gnaws away at our brains, our hearts, our souls. Brainwyrms, as Rumfitt would have it. In her story, 'A Unique Case of British Disease', Rumfitt follows in the shoes of a trans woman whose self-hatred has led her willingly into a wolf's den.

And it is the call of The Mothers, some strange sirens, who beckon Miren's protagonist in her new short story 'Mother'. Left without work by the pandemic, one sex worker gets lost in the funhouse mirror world of a certain mothering forum known best for its ability to hyper-radi-calise the middle class.

It is not safe to write about TERFs and SWERFs. Every trans writer in the UK I know — myself included — has been subject to deranged conspiracy theories, online harassment, and the occasional death threat. Meanwhile, sex worker writers work under pseudonyms, allow no photography at their own launch events, and face a barrage of accusations that they are part of a mysterious pimp lobby, or else risk potential arrest or problems crossing borders. But as Miren and Rumfitt explore in their ranging conversation that closes this collection, even our own are not necessarily safe. Taking as a case study what happened to science fiction writer Isabel Fall, whose single short story 'I Sexually Identify as an Attack Helicopter' caused one of the largest and most vicious online hate campaigns in recent memory, Miren and Rumfitt write about the tug-of-war between their desire to write truthfully and the potential of a backlash that loses all sense of proportion.

It's a dilemma that hits close to home. A creeping self-censorship has infected my own work. My words must be chosen with a level of care that grinds creativity to an almost full stop, for fear of kicking one or another of these hornet's nests — the TERFs, the SWERFs, and those who are so under attack within our own communities that they cannot help but lash out at anything that is critical or unfa-miliar. It is a self-censorship that makes me nervous even to write the introduction for a collection that includes a satirical depiction of a billionaire whose entire life revolves around trying to squash us all out of existence. But the truth is that we need this writing — we need writing that challenges power, that twists the moment to show us a new way of seeing, that holds a critical mirror up to our own weathered faces.

"It's easy to slip into reactionary thinking," Rumfitt writes to Miren. But so, too, is it easy to forget that challenging artistic expression is necessary to liberation.

Morgan M Page is a writer, historian, and artist based in London, England. She is the creator of One From the Vaults, *the podcast that brings you all of the dirt, gossip, and glamour from trans history. With Chase Joynt, she is the co-writer of the feature film* Framing Agnes *(Sundance, 2022) and the book* Boys Don't Cry *(MQUP, 2022). She is a life-long activist for sex workers' rights.*

MOTHER

FRANKIE MIREN

Have you ever woken knowing, deep in your tattered soul, that you are poison? Here's what it feels like: sallow light on your pillow, your oily scalp, the clenched claw of your hand, the sweet rotten smell of your cunt. It is dust on your bedside table, a flutter of greying net in the breeze, a book that is ring-marked with tea, sticky tendrils looking for prey. It is a stranger shouting on the street, a hunger for meat. It feels like relief, the arrival of Fate; the knowledge that today has come in from the night, will jump velvet-pawed through the window to slink into the world.

It is the morning lockdown ends, and this is happening to me.

I drag myself into sitting position and shuffle into the bathroom, imagining The Mothers watching me in approval. *Good girl. Stupid whore.* The bathroom walls are blue and my flatmate has hung fake ivy from the ceiling. The bathmat holds two perfect wet footprints and I sit on the edge of the bath to fit my feet into them, feeling as my flatmate must have done, wrapping a towel around herself, shaking drops of water into the air, planning her journey to work and

7

thinking about how, finally, we are allowed outside. Hers is a bright open day, a beginning and not an end.

In the mirror, there I am. *Dick receptacle.* I clean my teeth to spare myself from the stench, scrubbing until I spit flecks of blood. My hair looks singed and broken when I was sure it was lustrous, could swear I just curled it into ringlets. A brittle clump falls into the sink and I gather it into a ball to look closely: spidery threads clogged with sticky flakes of skin. And this, after all, is real. I watch my reflection smile – a snarl – her fingers bent into her mouth. With my teeth I tear a delicate rip of skin from the edge of my nail.

Our kitchen is windowless, like a casino, a place of yellow cheer. My flatmate and I have separate shelves in the fridge; hers full of batch-cooked chili and pasta, mine full of meat. I pull out a steak and slice it very thinly, an almost transparent layer, marbled with delicate lines of fat like the template of an ancient text, oozing blood. It is beautiful.

'What is all this?' My flatmate is waving at me, circling with her hand. 'Why? This was a vegetarian house.'

'Huh?' I try to formulate words but it is weeks since I spoke and my vocal chords rasp. I roll a slice of steak and suck until its colour changes from deep red to grey. My flat-mate's ear is shiny, its texture mismatched to her peach-fluff cheeks. I wonder if it is coated in wax, a protective layer that might make her waterproof. I cough up flecks of meat and my flatmate steps back.

'When did you last sleep?' She stands in the doorway with her clown's eyes all bulbous and wide. 'Have you slept?'

I shake my head. No, I never sleep, I cannot, have forgotten how. My brain zaps. Tinnitus like a ceaseless alarm; it's always time to be awake.

I cut a fatter slice of steak and fit the whole thing into my mouth.

'Are you going back to work?' Flatmate hovers. I know she's trying to be casual, always trying to be so woke about prostitution. I want to tell her the disgust that broils in her gut is right – she is with The Mothers – but I can't speak because my mouth is full of flesh.

That smell! I grab a bottle of disinfectant from under the sink and spray it on my hands, up my arms and behind my ears like perfume.

In my room I sit on the floor and check the forum, but The Mothers have moved on and I find no mention of whores today. I close the tab and open Instagram to immerse myself one last time with Casey in Melbourne, a stripper who does yoga and swims in rivers. It's been a while since I came here. I used to wonder how I could get a work visa for Australia and whether it was too late for me to learn pole tricks. I thought I could get a dog and I'd imagine feeling so limber and free, every interaction sensual, my movements painless and everything fresh and new. But it is over, a form that does not fit. The ocean and mountains disappear, the dog does not exist and my joints are seized rigid. Anyway I hate to leave the house. I will never visit Melbourne.

I stop half-way through dressing and slap my arms and legs. Little puffs of dust, dissolving skin cells, fly up. For sure, the rot is deep inside my bones. *Prostitutes are walking sex burgers. Just meat for sale.* The Mothers take a step closer. I feel them watching me, encircling me with their arms. *It's to your credit that you actually listen,* The Mothers would tell me, so kindly, words like apple pie.

I pack for work: lingerie, heels, flogger, paddle, whip, rope. A gallon of petrol.

★

Once, a long time ago, I was sunlight, beaming into men's lives and filling them with radiance. I was a healer, a sex witch, a warm tide, cooling rain. Looking back, I see myself reflected in an endless loop of hotel mirrors, my stomach taut, my tits bouncing. 'Oh god,' I'd say as I watched myself. 'So hot!'

It was the early 2000s and escort agencies were newly online, resplendent with low-quality pictures of hookers in Victoria's Secret. And we were out there with our Nokias, no longer carrying around clunky credit card imprinters in our handbags, ready for the digital age. I was into a blog by a New York escort called Suzie who whispered in my ear the sacred rites of sex, reminding me that prostitutes are god's chosen, that being a hooker was a noble cause. I'd stride out on bookings in my satin pencil skirt and blouse, into houses and flats and hotel rooms like a benevolent spirit. I'd come home in the early hours and imagine Suzie getting up and drinking coffee. I'd count my money and sense her approval. When I woke, I'd know she was just pulling on her stockings and I'd close my eyes and send positive vibes around the globe.

In Suzie I thought I had found myself. The shape of her world felt good, her words rolled out through my mouth, her walk was my walk, my hands, stretched into unaccustomed gestures, were animated by a new spirit. Sometimes I'd surprise myself, telling stories I wasn't sure were mine. I'd feel my limbs moving to an undulation that belonged to another life, another psyche. Once, talking to my mum, I'd found her staring in confusion, as though she didn't recognise the person before her. Now, of course, I see only the ill fit of that form. Suzie? We are nothing alike! Still, I miss her at times, her peppy chat, the generous spin she put on things.

The Mothers hiss in my ear.

No need. It is fifteen years since I felt the flicker of Suzie in my soul. The night it ended I was working a shift in a Mayfair hostess bar, a plush, intimidating place with a brightly-lit side-room in which clients would sit and we would file past like cattle. Suzie was already slipping away. I shuffled through the room that night but I wasn't really there in my young-ish, cute-ish body; I was waiting, waiting for a new understanding in which to pour myself. Still, in my young-ish, cute-ish body, I was chosen along with a tall girl whose name I never knew. A group of men took us back to a townhouse on a West London square. I remember white mansions, a pillared porch. It was Tory-paedo chic, a stale waft of jasmine in the night air. As we climbed the steps, I tried to remind myself I was a sex goddess, that I was making Suzie proud, but I remember seeing my cheapo heels and hearing them clippety-clop in the marble hallway and what I really felt was dread.

The men took us into this huge, creamy sitting room with fake orchids on side-tables. I remember looking out of the window at the lights in people's houses around the square. There was a garden in the middle, surrounded by a wrought iron fence, and I wondered what would happen if I ran into the middle of it, scratched my way through the roses, and screamed.

'Dance for us,' one of the men said. 'A sexy dance.'

'Tssk. No.' The tall girl waved her hand dismissively. I was impressed! I didn't know we were allowed to say no.

The guys weren't having it though. They believed beyond doubt that by agreeing to come back to their mansion, we would do whatever they asked. So we got up and danced, the two of us, gyrating around the room while they slouched on sofas and bored into us with their eyes. The tall girl was crying, just slowly taking off her clothes and lifting her arms in the air and arching her back, but all the time with tears streaming down her face. She looked very stately and made no sound but her face was streaked with mascara. And I realised Suzie was gone. My limbs, without her, were unwieldly and graceless. I didn't know how to hold my face. The guys didn't notice or didn't care and after a while they took us into the bedrooms and fucked us. And the thing was, we'd planned to fuck them – that was our job – it was the dance that had tipped us over the edge. And it was just a dance, you'll probably say, and a dance is surely less than a fuck? But the point was we hadn't agreed to it and then, suddenly, we had no choice.

On the way home we realised we were catching the same night bus and the tall girl looked furious. 'I don't want to chat,' she said as she climbed the steps to the upper deck, 'about this or that'. *I don't want to chat about this or that.* I sat two rows behind her and looked at the back of her neck and at her reflection in the window which was very still. Myself, I had no reflection. I was an empty, monstrous chasm, I was a soulless void. And if I'd have known to look out and at the sky, in that state of grace, I'd have seen Fate turn its eyes to me.

★

Outside my room, my flatmate is speaking to her boyfriend. Nonsense syllables rise and fall. I mutter to myself. 'I don't want to chat about this or that.'

The voices in the hallway stop and I know they must have heard me. 'I don't want to chat!' I shout, dragging myself to my feet. I fling open the door, 'About this or that!' My voice sounds phlegmy. A frog in my throat.

I used to speak. Before the pandemic, I joined a sex worker collective, at first sitting silently in meetings, beady-eyed like an owl, and then taking up space – not too much, just enough to remind myself I exist. I'd never thought about the politics of hooking before, or not consciously. Suzie was political in her way, but the collective made sense of the whole world. I saw the spider's web of power in which we were all enmeshed. Back then I'd have told you we were flies, half-paralysed but still struggling as our killers advanced, dancing, dancing in their glare. Now I know different. With every tweet – *Can't wait to see my lovely clients again! Email me now, lovers! Xx* – I throw a silky skein of entrapment. With each paid-for fuck, I spread my venom.

I check my phone but no Mother has messaged for days. Perhaps their work is done.

I once felt so welcome. Early in lockdown, I followed a link and found myself with The Mothers. Of course I'd heard about them before, but I'd never sought their company. On the forum, I found stories about births and deaths and diets and DIY; about toddlers, teenagers, celebrities and dog walkers; about breakdowns and baby names, and husbands and nannies and really all of The Mothers' life, and it was a particular life, not my own or even a life I could ever achieve, but one which came to seem the blueprint of womanhood.

What marked The Mothers as an irresistible force was their anger at all they believed existed in opposition to the blueprint. They were angry with men, but this was of no note; it was their anger with women that set them apart. Sometimes the blueprint seemed such a fragile flower. I would hold my breath as I typed. The Mothers were angry with trans women and they were angry with sex workers. It felt like coming home; they were angry with me.

The day I joined them was at the height of lockdown. I hadn't eaten and was light-headed, cramped over as digestive fluids attacked my empty stomach. It felt spiritual, as though I was cleansed and amorphous, ready, waiting. And there, in the references and articles, in the many, many forum posts, I found new form.

You whores pander to men, you undermine women, you steal our husbands, you spread disease, you are a constant threat to society and morals. How can women ever be judged on their intellect when sluts make money selling their bodies … there's no such thing as an honest whore.

Both the spider and the fly. The sheets wrapped around my legs like web, my body ripe with venom, flesh eating flesh.

Would you consider selling your orifices for money the same as working at McDonalds? pondered one Mother. They were so philosophical. I thought about McDonalds and my stomach rumbled.

To be more precise, another one replied, *prostitutes rent the use of their orifices (and breasts etc). If they were to sell certain body parts, the buyer would presumably take them with him.*

A hand under my T-shirt, I squeezed my breasts, the silicone of my implants moving beneath my skin like a creature trapped. I imagined someone taking home one of my tits, borrowing it for a designated time with instructions on keeping it alive, a blood supply to hook it up to, a tank of fluid in which to keep it. I didn't think that sounded bad. Easier, in fact, than having to stay attached to it for a whole booking.

There was no doubt, I was an abomination.

★

I don't leave the house until long after my flatmate is gone. When I do, I step out and sniff the air, blinking in the unaccustomed light. I swear the houses across the road have moved, their numbers no longer logical. I stifle a laugh.

I take the bus into work, although the tube would be faster. I cannot be without phone signal when so much is at stake, though minute on minute go by and no message appears. Still, when I glance out of the window I see that fate runs beside me, lopes down pavements and across roads with eyes like suns. Fate runs on night paws and no one hears the wakening thud of that heart, feels its hot breath in their hair. This bright burning thing is mine alone.

I scour the forum for signs. I read an old post: *The less we see of prostitutes the better.* There is nothing new.

In The Mothers' silence, I feel suddenly alone. I remember that night bus, the back of the tall girl's head. And through that emptiness, I think about RJ. I should know better but I find myself searching for them, turning in my seat as people climb onto the bus, scanning the faces of passers-by. I'm cold, as if I were back under the icy December rain in which we met.

It was pre-pandemic, a sex work protest, and I was carrying a banner. I found myself walking next to this person in a waterproof coat whose hands were red and raw from the cold, their knuckles bony white as they gripped their own sign.

'Why are you here?' I'd asked them and I'd expected them to say what we were all saying. *It's the apocalypse. So many dead sex workers in France and no one cares. And the Nordic Model is gonna come here too. And that fucking election, all that wasted canvassing and now a full on fascist government. Things can't get worse!* But RJ looked confused, a startled little field-dweller in my glare, and I knew then that they were like me.

After the protest RJ invited me back to their place. I nearly said no; it had been years since I was in some-one's house and I wasn't sure I'd remember what to do. I'd memorised the right things to say in meetings, and on bookings clients didn't care as long as I listened and smiled, but being a guest would be different. Still, that thunderous sky and the feeling that this was the end of days made me say yes and then there we were.

*

RJ lived in a house-share in Brockley. When we got back, they made us tea and we sat in their room looking out of the window. Someone had hung white shirts out to dry at the back of a house opposite, a whole row of them now soaking, their arms waving in the storm. They must have been work shirts, someone's uniform. We got stoned and gradually it got dark but we could still see those sodden ghosts, hanging from the line by a single arm and, even-tually, falling to the ground.

I saw RJ a lot after that. A few months later, they got a dog, Cleo, a jumpy, rangy sighthound-cross from Battersea

Dogs Home who barked at leaves that skittered across the pavement. We took long walks around the park, not speaking much, just throwing sticks for Cleo and smiling at each other. RJ wasn't like anyone I'd met before – though, in fairness, I hadn't had many real-life friends. RJ didn't tell me what they thought and they didn't ask for my opinions; we would just float around near each other, formless but happy.

Then one night, sitting in RJ's room, in the jumping flame of a candle, I had a memory of being a teenager. For a few years, I'd been obsessed with the Ouija board. I had this group of friends who began slicing little cuts in our fingers and exchanging blood. We'd gather in bedrooms, or in graveyards, or bus shelters, getting stoned on the 90s soapbar hash that was all we could get back then. The Ouija glass always moved and the spirits were close.

'I used to do that too!' RJ said and it was another strand in the web that bound us together. 'I honestly believed I was some sort of Satan worshipper!'

We both laughed but RJ carried on. 'The way we took on this made-up thing – I mean, it was just some media panic – and then it was real. It's who we thought we were.' They lay back on the floor so their face was in darkness. 'Did you do that?'

I didn't answer.

'It's the same when you're a whore,' RJ said from the floor. 'All these horrors and fears and hatred of women are wrapped around us. And even if we fight against it, the fight only traps us more, makes the knots tighter. I sometimes feel like I'm just a collection of fragments from other people's brains. Like my psyche would collapse without them. You get that? I know you do.'

A car alarm was going off outside and someone was playing music in the kitchen. RJ was saying my name as I got up and left. I saw myself tumbling through darkness, stumbling in my pleasers, trying to find a door that would take me into the world. RJ called out but I knew I would never go back.

★

Soon after that night, the pandemic hit and I no longer had any reason to leave the house. I straggled together enough money for rent doing cam work and selling content online. And since RJ had been my only friend, I no longer had any need to speak. My flatmate, I could communicate with via text and, occasionally, by leaving written notes in the fridge, tucked under her tubs of chili.

I spent hours looking for someone new. Casey from Melbourne was intense and, for a while, I could feel the Australian sun on my face. I'd be surprised when I looked in the mirror and saw my own features, my own body, my hair that didn't, after all, hang in sculpted curls down my back. In my confusion, I threw a t-shirt over the mirror.

Gradually, I let my other bondings disintegrate. Lying rank under my sheets or sitting cross-legged on my bedroom floor, I unfollowed and unfollowed until only The Mothers remained. Days passed, weeks, months. I started eating my meals in the middle of the night, in our casino kitchen, realising one day I no longer needed to consume anything green. I survived on whole chickens, cooked inexpertly in our greasy oven, on discounted cuts of beef, pork, salmon, tuna. Shitting was difficult and I began every day with a glycerine suppository up my arse.

Only RJ kept contacting me and, eventually, even they gave up.

★

Today, I get off the bus near the incall and walk slowly. The pavement glitters. My presence disturbs people, like soap poured into grease. I see children pulled away as I pass, a shop door closes in my face. Little scenes flash into my head that don't seem attached to anything. I see a small girl laying a table in a house I don't recognise, lining up knives and forks and looking through a doorway into a kitchen that is lit with an orangey glow. I see a ladybird on a hand; the inside of an airport; a woman running with a bag.

I put my hands up like blinkers, panting in relief when I reach the darkness of the flat. I get ready half-heartedly. My teeth stained with lipstick, a robe with torn lace. In the mirror, I look like a carcass dug up from the earth and draped for Halloween. That stench, the rot of flesh.

A man arrives. His outline is hazy, his mouth moves but I cannot decipher its sounds. I tie him to the bed and he looks surprised so I wrap a stocking over his eyes and ball the other into his mouth. I sit astride him and tear another strip of flesh from the side of my nail. It's a health hazard; if I jerk him off I could get jizz in this open wound. The thought makes me angry and I slap him around the face. His dick gets hard.

I catch sight of the scene in the mirror, his body inert beneath me, my fangs bared.

'This is what The Mothers want,' I scrape a nail along his chest.

'Mmm,' he spits out the stocking. 'A nun role play? Very sexy.'

'No!' I slap him again and shove the stocking so far down his throat he begins to choke. 'Stupid man.'

The Mothers are close, they pat my head. *Stupid girl, filthy whore.*

I light candles, so many of them, flickering pillars that fill the flat with dancing shadows. Outside, a car honks its horn and someone shouts. I bite another nail down to the quick and my blood tastes like wine. I remember the candlelight morphing RJ's features so that one minute they looked happy, another sad, angry, mean, excited, gentle, kind. As if they didn't exist outside this hologram of flame.

When I've lit every candle in the flat I feel that the end is close. This morning seems a long time ago, my bed, my flatmate, the clothes on my bedroom floor. Fate is here, and I am glad.

With his arms and legs spread-eagled, the man on the bed is still struggling. Spit drools from his mouth, my stocking like vomited entrails. I suck the cuts on my finger and they give me strength. I am my own energy-source. We whores, after all, are both blood-sucker and meat. I think, perhaps, I can stay here forever, like a snake eating its tail, gradually fading but, for a while, an eternity.

A dog barks outside and I think of Cleo. I think of the spider, the fly, the snake, the frog in my throat; all animals reduced to glyphs for human life, unreal as whores. For second I waver. I imagine untying the man and walking out of here, taking the train to Brockley, knocking on RJ's door and stepping back in time, before I knew The Mothers, before Fate, larger than us all, began to slink through the world.

But that creature cannot be banished. It brushes up against my thigh, so soft.

I pour petrol slowly and delicately, a circle around the room, a sacred space, a ritual purification. The man is writhing on the bed. I let wax pour over my bitten hands and I tilt a candle to the floor.

'Goodbye, Mothers,' I say, and they hiss in assent.

A UNIQUE CASE OF BRITISH DISEASE

ALISON RUMFITT

"It's so wonderful to see you... um, Sam," said the woman with the short brown hair who opened the door to her. Samantha smiled and thanked her quietly in a voice she had carefully crafted to sound as meek as possible. When she'd been putting it together, she'd thought of old nursery rhymes and idioms about church mice. As she aged, her voice seemed to be getting deeper despite itself, and so she spoke even quieter, every word pronounced as softly as humanly possible, like she was scared she might startle somebody.

"Thank you," she said, and stepped through the open door. "It's good to see you too. Must have been, oh, since that conference in Birmingham."

"Yes," said the woman, who had turned from her and was now walking down the corridor.

She hadn't offered to take her coat, so Samantha hung it herself from one of the golden hooks to her right. There were lots of coats already there, and only one of the hooks wasn't tripled down with them. She hung hers carefully, trying to guess which coat belonged to which person, as the woman descended the stairs at the end of the corridor without bothering to check if Samantha was following. When she did go after her she walked carefully and softly, trying to avoid what she had heard someone once term as the *flat-footed thumping of men's steps*. Ever since that phrase had been uttered in her earshot it had wormed its way into the front of her head; every time she was walking in public or around other people she remembered it and adjusted accordingly.

The stairs were lined with paintings of pastoral scenes which went, rather elegantly, she thought, from day at the top of the stairs to night at the bottom, where the dining room and kitchen were. The dining room opened out into a large garden, or as large as was reasonably attainable for a London townhouse situated on a slope, with the garden a whole level below the front door. A quirk of the borough. From the road you had a near-unobstructed view of the heath and if you squinted very hard you might catch a sight of Marx's giant head between the trees down the hill, permanently looking in the vague direction of Douglas Adams' grave, from what she remembered. The last time she had been to the cemetery had been a week or so after a man from Twitter (who she followed, and who followed her) had tried to attack Marx's face with a hammer and succeeded in breaking off his nose. It hadn't been repaired yet. There had been talks among some ministers about removing it altogether. That same man had come to some of these meetings, once upon a time. The more formal ones than this, which was more of a casual drinks-and-chat event.

Samantha came to the bottom of the stairs and saw all of them there, already assembled around the table, chatting, sipping at their flutes. They turned to look at her. Men and women, looking at her.

"Hi Sam," one of them said, and smiled like the Cheshire Cat. Jean. The woman who owned the house, the one who had opened the door for her, was named Lily. She saw all these people rarely, and mainly interacted with them on Twitter – she matched their faces to their profile images and the names associated with them. Kenneth. Helen. Paloma. Scott. A second Helen. Kathy. A third Helen. A Helena. No Jennifer. She wondered if Jennifer wasn't coming after all, but then she heard Lily saying "Jen's just texted saying she'll be a little late."

She was the only transsexual here and she knew that some of the people in the room wouldn't even want to call her that, except maybe begrudgingly because they didn't want to call her a man in drag to her face. They'd happily call other people men in drag to their faces, but not her, because she would join in, and that meant she was invited to things like this, got to sit at their table and drink from their flutes of wine and sometimes write a piece for the *Times*. Kenneth, who, at that moment, was purposefully looking elsewhere when she sat down at the table, had once put his hand on her hip and said that she was one of the better ones. She had felt sick later that night knowing she wished he'd kept going, but that he was more drunk than she, that no one ever seemed to want to kiss her unless they were that drunk, and even then, they didn't want to follow through. She drank from her glass. The windows into the garden were open, and, as the night was coming down, moths started to flutter in around the strip lighting in the ceiling. Her head hurt looking at the lights for too long. Her head hurt now whenever she opened Twitter, just a twinge, but what of it. She didn't use it because she wanted to.

"I think we're seeing real progress," said Helen2, "especially now we have so many ministers that agree with us. The big issue is how many agree with us but don't do anything about it, you know. They just agree with us, sometimes like our Tweets and take flack for that. But when we're out on the streets yelling… where are they then?"

"Well," Helena said, "that's why Jennifer is so good. Not a minister, true, but she might as well be."

"Probably more powerful than a minister."

"Probably."

Everyone nodded in agreement. Samantha did too, but she kept her mouth shut. Every time she spoke around these people without being directly asked a question, she felt their eyes stabbing into her, as if her simply speaking, almost always in agreement, was grossly offensive. She did agree with them! But she supposed sometimes that wasn't good enough. She couldn't hate them for thinking of her as a man because she too thought of herself as a man often enough, and with what was likely to be far more ferocious intensity than any of them could muster. Sometimes, recently, the inside of her skull seemed to be a constant repeating thought that was simply *man man man man* whenever she saw herself in the reflection of, say, a shop window or a car door or or or. She could see herself faintly in the glass of her drink. She could hear what Helen1 was thinking when she looked at her.

"What do you think other right-minded transsexuals like you have to do?" Helen1 asked, looking right at her. A moth was fluttering about above the woman's head, a large one, white with black spots across its wings, and in the light it looked larger still than it probably was.

She swallowed a mouthful of drink. "Well," she said, making sure her voice was neither too loud nor too deep, "I do think we are trying. You know, every time I see someone being misogynist in the name of transsexual causes, I tell them what they're doing. I try to distribute as much feminist writing as I can to other transsexuals who perhaps might be potentially persuaded or do not have much of a political engagement. But it's an uphill battle. I think the lines are getting further apart. And what's worse is that I see so many of them – transactivists, transgenderists – now calling themselves transsexuals proudly, some of them without even bothering to go through the process. Which is quite offensive, really."

"But what are you doing to combat the misogyny?"

"I mean, calling it out, as I said. Every time I see it. Do you... think I, we, could be doing more?"

"Yes," said Helen.

"What?"

"I think that's more on you to answer," she said.

Lily cut in. "We're very grateful to have you," she said. "You're wonderful company and you speak so well on things."

She knew that they used her to prove a point. That was why she was invited to speak at things. It wasn't because they liked her. Lily only cut in now because Helen was speaking too close to the actual fact of things.

If you know they hate you Samantha, if you know why they always shorten your name to Sam, why come here at all? Why not disengage? Let the transsexual tide turn away from you? Become anonymous? Delete Twitter?

Kenneth sent her a picture of his flaccid penis once, unprompted, asking if she thought that mole was anything to worry about.

"No you're right," she said, "Helen's right. We do need to do more. But I don't want to get in the way, you know. I don't want to dominate the conversation. I don't want to make anyone uncomfortable, so sometimes I just sit back and let you talk, make sure my presence makes things clear that transsexuals *do* agree with you. But yes. We can do more."

The moth landed on the very top of Helen's head. "There's a moth in your hair," she said.

Helen's hand shot up and grabbed it in her fist, as fast as anything she had seen. She moved her hand away and tightened it, crushing the white moth inside between her fingers and her palm, the dust from its wings smearing between her forefinger and thumb. It was such a strange, sudden action that Samantha found herself unsure if she was going to say anything more or if her little speech was finished. Helen opened her hand and let the crushed insect fall onto the table. It was barely recognisable as a moth anymore, just a mass of brown stuff squished into a ball with a couple of little legs, like tiny tendrils, reaching out.

"What?" asked Helen.

"Oh, just… that was fast," smiled Samantha.

"I hope Jen arrives soon," said Scott from the far end of the table, evidently bored of anything she had to say.

Jen. Jennifer Caldwell, valiant high-priestess of the movement (such as there was a movement). Samantha had been around her a couple of times now, but she had never spoken a word to her, only smiled and nodded politely before turning off to speak to someone else. Nevertheless, Samantha had read everything she had ever written, despite not having any interest in children's fantasy literature; it was practically a rule. If you were on a videochat and you didn't have Caldwell's books framed clearly behind you, you would face some form of disciplinary action. Twelve books about a little girl and her witch friends, which started off mostly whimsical and ended up as strangely violent holocaust allegories in which witches were burned alive in ovens – Samantha found those sickening, in all honesty, but Jennifer was Jennifer after all. Once those books were finished, she continued writing but for adults now, working on another series of books about rural life and local council politics, books which critics either thought were shockingly dull or wonderfully witty.

Five years ago, Caldwell had, reportedly, contacted Helen1, who had written an article for the *Telegraph Online* about women's prisons. Caldwell had questions for Helen – the article had made her feel shocked and scared in a way things rarely did. She started to read and converse with the Gender Critical side more often, always in private up until quite recently, when she had come out publicly through her work. In her latest rural council satire there had been an extended plot thread about a man who dressed as a woman to enter a WI meeting, and, facing criticism from TRAs, Caldwell had become more public about her beliefs around trans women, sex workers, socialists and anti-zionist wonks.

Helen2 had painted a picture of her, haloed by golden light, surrounded by hordes of grateful women bowing their heads. Scott had become quite grumpy about the whole thing, given that, before Jennifer went public with her beliefs, he was by far the most famous individual in their loose circle of intellects.

The knowledge that Jennifer (Jennifer!) would be here soon had charged the dining room with an electric energy. Everyone was shifting and moving and trying to get comfortable, and the conversations were quiet and brief. See, nobody wanted to say anything important when Jennifer wasn't within earshot. This was what had happened: the group had restructured itself around its new celebrity member, centring her, suddenly, and side-lining others. Many members of the group felt a mix of emotions about this. Many were resentful that someone so relatively new to the ideology, with more undeveloped thoughts, was now its de facto leader. Many too were jealous that Caldwell enjoyed the benefits of her wealth, in the billions, whilst some of them had faced losing their jobs for their beliefs. The finale of the film series adapting her children's fantasy novels was coming out soon. A journalist and opinion writer had said that the film was a torch in the darkness of today's growing fascism, and compared the current Prime Minister to Rasputin, the books' antagonist. Jennifer Caldwell walked with ten thousand shining wings fluttering at her back. Jennifer Caldwell was the rose with her red hair and ate men like air. They could all feel the pulsing through the earth as Jennifer Caldwell got closer and closer, her taxi turning onto the street. When she passed a streetlamp its light bulged and burst through its proximity to her. She sucked the breath from your lungs. She crushed pimps and traffickers beneath her sensible shoes. She struck through Stonewall and the BDS movement with a sword made of pure and blinding light.

They all waited for her arrival in silence now. Nobody had anything to say. They awaited her until they heard the bell ring out, signalling her imminent arrival. Lily disappeared up the stairs, nearly tripping over herself in her rush to the front door. When she was gone, they all held their breath and Samantha wished for a strange moment that they might all put out their hands and clasp them together so that they formed an unbroken ring. Lily reappeared, scurrying down the stairs, and behind her came Jennifer like a walking God, a walking Twitter account, a thing with billions upon billions of pounds and clout and influence, a hot wet dripping woman made from woman-bits. Also, a natural blonde with blue eyes, about five foot six, less wrinkles than would be expected due to injections of Botox and Juvéderm. A normal woman, an adult human female, very material. You could, if you liked, reach out and touch her, but Samantha wouldn't ever do that. It was hard enough just existing in its presence, this pure and unfiltered ideal of modern womanhood. Normal and extranormal. Reality and the breaking of. 'A remarkable case of British disease', a Corbynite had once said of her on Twitter.

"Hello everyone," she said, and something inside each of their heads twitched at the sound of her voice. One thing or many things; they responded to her words like locusts swarming. Samantha felt the pain inside her skull, the same pain she felt often when she logged on Twitter, sharp, moving around the front of her brain.

She only had one of them, and a smaller one at that; spare a thought for Helen1 who, through exposure and sheer zealotry, had between ten or twenty of the things inside her head. They were usually small and discrete but in the presence of Caldwell they swelled up and wriggled frantically inside there, large enough and violent enough that they were clearly visible as a quivering lump on her forehead, right between her eyes. And Jennifer herself? Well. It would be impossible to count how many of them she had. But she seemed remarkably calm most of the time, despite her infestation, which sometimes pressed against the insides of her eyeballs, or spilled out of her ears or down her nose, dribbling a clear white liquid that she wiped away, embarrassed, hoping nobody had seen it. It was all about proximity, you see. She had been in direct contact, she'd let it touch her and had touched it all over in return, meaning that more and more parasites grew within her head. A colony of them. And those who were then in contact with her, such as Helen or Lily, grew some themselves, especially as they hung on her every word (they could travel through words, spoken and written, they could jockey on the backs of phrases).

Samantha, poor Samantha, there sometimes but rarely spoken to directly... she only had a couple. Slim pickings. Enough to make her head hurt and to drive her into angry, hours-long frenzies on Twitter, but not enough to make her truly transcendent. She could not see those strange geographies the same way the Helens could. The Helens perceived colours that Samantha could not. Poor Samantha, useful only as a tick on a form, an example of the woke posturing she so hated. What was the point, she wondered, when the doubt crept over her, when she was lying alone and awake. What was the real point of alienating all those with shared experiences over a quibble around the particularities of those experiences? She claimed to interviewers that many transsexuals believed what she did, because it was hard to prove either way; but in reality, over the course of her life she had maybe met only ten who did, and three of them had died in the past decade, two from cancer and one from suicide.

Jennifer looked around the room, her gaze brushing across each of them in turn. She nodded at every person.

Kenneth let out a little yelp when she nodded at him, which Samantha thought was pathetic, but nobody commented on it. But then her gaze fell upon Samantha, and not only did she nod but she spoke to her, said her name. "Hello, Samantha," she said. Her full name! No shortened, ambiguously gendered *Sam* here. *Samantha,* spoken by their very own Priestess, preacher, angel, saviour.

"Hi," she said, in a quiet voice.

"It's so good to see you," Jennifer said.

"It's good to see you too."

"I'm glad to see you didn't start without me," she said to the room.

"We wouldn't dream of it," said the Helens as one, their voices aligned perfectly in pitch and tone and rhythm. "We've let him be part of it all for too long."

"I agree," said Kenneth. "You know once we were drunk after an event, and he tried to pull me into a taxi with him? He had his hands around my waist and everything."

"I just hate when she speaks, you know," said Lily. "He always speaks so loudly, and so deep, a loud, deep voice, speaking over everyone else."

They were moving in on her now. Samantha looked around and saw the three Helens hop up on top of the table, crouched, arms towards her, creeping forwards. Kenneth and Scott were either side of her. All of them, encircling her, whilst Jennifer looked on from above like the eye of God gazing down.

"I don't understand!" shouted Samantha, looking for somewhere to run to, but there was nowhere to run to.

They were creeping up on her from every side. Their hands were nearly touching her.

"You're a man, Sam," said Lily.

"S–so's Kenneth! So's Scott!"

"But at least they admit it."

They pounced. Samantha fell to the floor, scrabbling and pushing against them, but to no avail. They were pressing down on her firmly, both men had her arms, and the Helens were sitting on her legs. She was looking up into their faces and saw the violent lumps in between their eyes, the dribbling liquid that came out of their eyes and ears and noses and mouths. Jennifer walked to her and looked down at her, and the little white worms themselves were hanging loosely from her orifices, wriggling in the air on lines of mucus. When she spoke her voice was wet, it bubbled out of her throat, dripping spit down onto poor little Samantha's face.

"Sam," Jennifer said, "it's nothing personal, you know?"

MORBID
OBSESSIONS:
A CONVERSATION

FRANKIE:

Hey Alison! We decided to do this project together because we felt an affinity with each other's first books, *Tell Me I'm Worthless* and *The Service*. For me, seeing the way you'd fictionalised personal and community pain and dissected the awfulness of current discourse around trans rights through this wild and horrifying tale, really struck home. And our short stories, without planning, also have a strong crossover.

So, woo!, excited to have this conversation about bigotry!

It's hard not to be morbidly obsessed with the people who hate you, especially when they're so visible and relentless. Some of the mega-SWERFs loom so large and I've spent a lot of time wondering how you'd end up in that place, feeling entitled to talk over people's lived experience and so blinded by ideology you've lost all sense of perspective. Right now, we've got the threat of a clause in the Online Safety Bill which would basically make online advertising of sex work illegal. It's beyond nightmarish – that is how pretty much everyone I know finds clients – and it's such a perfect example of SWERF myopia. Their obsession with prostitution is so intense we are no longer real people with day-to-day needs like paying bills and eating; sex work is seen as so evil the industry must be eradicated at all costs. Even if that cost means destitution for the very people they're trying to 'protect'.

Almost always, SWERFs and TERFs are the same people. Maybe it's easiest to see the crossovers of these ideologies at their sharpest, where they coalesce in this mythical figure who must be criminalised out of existence: the sex worker; the trans woman; the racialised trans sex worker who bears the brunt of violence. This figure is seen as pathological, a warped version of womanhood. And, around the world, the effects of this are so visible in the profiling of trans women and WOC who are harassed and arrested for prostitution. SWERFs and TERFs don't engage with the realities of why women, and particularly trans women, sell sex, or only engage as an afterthought to their conception of this mythical hate figure who tells us about nothing but the state of their own psyches.

So neither of us is a trans sex worker, and I'm very conscious of not wanting to speak for anyone else, but it feels important to acknowledge here how many trans people do sell sex. And also to acknowledge how much the sex worker rights movement owes to trans women, and how it's tied to wider queer liberation movements. So many hookers took part in Stonewall. Marsha P. Johnson and Sylvia Rivera were sex workers. These are not separate communities.

We talked about using the satanic panic as a theme for this book – and both of our stories have some satanic panic vibes! – so it was useful for me to stop and think about whether the lens of moral panic works for SWERFs in the way it does for TERFs, and to what extent those ideologies overlap.

There's moral panic in the fact that SWERFs single out prostitution as being this unique locus of exploitation, and the language they use to talk about sex work is pure bloodthirsty fearmongering. Still, lots of people do treat sex as something outside the realm of other social behaviour, and, sure, that's a product of a specific time and place, but telling women they're prudish or 'wrong' to feel this way feels downright rapey. It's great to imagine a world in which sex is not so fraught for so many people, but we're not there yet! I've seen some of this discourse from activists, and the idea that all sex workers should have this chill and easy relationship to sex is wild. Being sex positive, as in rejecting the culture of slut-shaming and fighting for bodily autonomy, isn't incompatible with having complicated personal feelings about sex. I've met so many hookers who are really fucking traumatised by sex and not the least bit *liberated*. I'll put my hand up to being one of them; for all intents and purposes I'm asexual these days and haven't had recreational sex in years. I love telling people I hate sex! Like telling people I hate Shakespeare (also true).

There has to be a way to argue for decrim and to tear apart SWERF ideology without demanding some weird allegiance to the sex industry. There have been times sex work felt like a space I could enact this ideal version of myself and that was, I guess, *empowering*. (That word has been trampled to death, I know). I don't feel like that now. The money, though, has been life-changing and allowed me such a different life from the one I'd have had otherwise. So, some hookers feel like sex work is a force for good, some don't. Hey ho. Likewise the fashion industry. In the meantime, policing and criminalisation are making sex workers' lives more dangerous, austerity is forcing people into sex work, closed borders and psychopathic immigration policy are enabling traffickers – it's a privilege to be able to sit here musing about the *meaning* of transactional sex.

Where moral panic does map onto SWERF ideology is the idea of the 'pimp lobby'; this belief that activists are backed by some shadowy faction of pimps and managers, whereas in reality we're all doing unpaid activism and paying our bills giving blowjobs. It allows them to discredit everything we say because we're just privileged puppets who are too brainwashed or too callous to care about our sisters who are chained to radiators.

In 'Mother', I wasn't trying to get inside the SWERF psyche like I was in *The Service* but this is what I'd love to talk to you about first: how it felt writing a TERF character in *Tell Me I'm Worthless*, and in 'A Unique Case of British Brain'; how you tried to make sense of their views; and where the line is between writing fiction that tries to understand a dangerous ideology and actually becoming an apologist for those views.

ALISON:

I'm writing this specifically on Saturday 26th March. Yesterday I woke up in a flat with the Virgin Mary watching over me (well, an icon of her). The day was hot. I was hungover. The previous night I had vomited into an attractive woman's sink. I left her flat in the morning and walked in the sun across towards New Cross, with the twin aim of 1) getting breakfast and an iced coffee of some description and 2) popping into The Word, a bookshop I like near Goldsmiths. In The Word I got myself a copy of the novel *I Who Have Not Known Men* by Jacqueline Harpman. I am usually resistant to dystopias that involve gender (more on that later) but I've been assured this one is good (if it isn't I'll have a go at some people). When, lightheaded, I got to a cafe, I checked Twitter for the first time in maybe an hour and a half, and I saw that Putin had made reference to JK Rowling in a speech. It's been the thing my timeline has been talking about since then but in that moment, I felt like I was struggling to get a grip on reality. It was difficult to believe the banal ridiculousness of it all. I find this is a regular reaction I have to the world now, and I worry if, perhaps it is a reactionary one. I don't mean that it is reactionary to hate that, say, something maddening happened in relation to JKR, but that the impulse to look at the world and think or say "this is fucking stupid" is reactionary. It's easy to accidentally slip into reactionary thinking.

It's easy to inhabit a reactionary mindset in fiction because of that, partly. People who are bigoted in some way are not materially different to you, beyond that they may or may not be in position of more significant material means. I didn't want to make the TERF character in *Tell Me I'm Worthless* rich because it would, I think, have made it harder for me to empathise with her mindset. That's not the case in what I'm writing now, of which 'British Brain' is a part; this is more satirical and thus I get to push the grotesquery of the upper classes to the logical extreme; oozing, dribbling, that sort of thing. Ila in *Tell Me I'm Worthless* was a project in trying to construct someone to inhabit an ideological framework but who would not feel like a pure ideological experiment. I don't know if that worked but it did for me. I do like Ila, somewhat. It was fun writing her, fun fleshing her out from a series of notes into something that resembled, to an extent, a real human. Did you feel this way with Paula? Both of our books use separate character perspectives to explore different relationships to a problem, but I thiiiiiink that we also both manage to make these people feel true enough to the reader that the trick works.

I should mention: the fiction piece that's part of this by me was originally part of my next novel *Brainwyrms*. I'm not actually even sure if it's going to be part of it any more, given that by the nature of novel writing I'm having to strip it back and focus on more particular ideas. I still think it's a pretty fun piece though! The focus of *Brainwyrms* has been revamped, as it were, to make it a book primarily, if not purely, about sex. Okay, not about sex, about *fucking* specifically. I just wrote a line that I like which may change, but currently reads *It used to be called being a sex worker, now it's just called being a faggot.*

Neither of us is a trans sex worker, no. You are a sex worker and I am a transsexual. I have *done* sex work, although not to an extent where I could ever identify as being someone who does it if that makes sense. So I still lack, to use a GIC term against them, *lived experience.* But given our respective communities' histories, as you said, it's vital that we formulate dialogue and solidarity. Our communities and identities are not separate. With increasing SWERF/TERF bills and right-wing violence, the people who are going to be hit first and hardest will be trans sex workers. I say *will be* but of course, they *are* being hit the hardest already. We should do everything we can to show solidarity to them.

The line between exploring these views and espousing them, though, is pretty clear to me, even if it maybe isn't to some readers. It's obvious that Ila is wrong because the reader can see her being effectively groomed, first by other TERFs and then by Albion itself. I was worried the scene of her being nearly assaulted in the bathroom by an older cis woman TERF would end up feeling too obvious, but a scene like that, which undoes the fallacies of the ideology, was needed I think. I do think TERFs are wrong about everything, but there is a root to their argument which they, likely without realising, share with a lot of trans arguments. A lot of TERFs talk at length about not feeling like women, not feeling any sort of association with it as a category or role beyond their biology. This makes me sad! But we are passed the point of ever fulfilling the dream of them realising on mass that this is exactly what trans people often feel. If there ever was an opportunity for that, it's gone. How do you feel about the prospect of engaging with SWERFs? Have you ever talked to them? Have you ever felt like you were successful in getting them to understand your position?

FRANKIE:

I loved knowing where you were and what headspace you were in when you wrote that (though solidarity with puking in a sink and being judged by Virgin Mary!) It made me think about how important it is to situate yourself in an argument. My views on sex work have changed so much over the years; sometimes I feel like I'm gaslighting my younger self, who I near enough accuse of false-consciousness these days. She'd have thought I was a bitter, uptight bitch. And maybe I am! But looking back I can see how any set of views you end up with is a product of the times, of who you're mates with, where you work, what state your health is in, what drugs you're taking. And in 'Mother' I wanted to take that to its illogical extreme. But while I'm here, I wanted to ask if you ever think about looking back at what you write now in 20 years? Can you imagine having a complete political turnaround and renouncing everything you once said?

Right now, I'm just back from a consultation with a surgeon to get my breast implants removed. He was rude and patronising and I ended up walking out, so I'm at my most anxious and jittery today. But anyway this surgery is on the cards for me because my chronic illness has got so debilitating I'm ready to take a gamble that it's my implants. Gutted though I am to lose my perfect tits, they're coming out! And that's important because I'm going to use that to draw a line under doing sex work. It'll be 27 years since I started in the industry (that's longer than you've been alive, right?) which honestly feels a bit horrifying!

So I'm thinking about how, maybe, being at this point allows me to say what I think about sex work with less fear of repercussion from clients. I definitely toned down *The Service* because I was still working. Though I was reeling when several clients read it, carried on booking me, but needed layer upon layer of extra reassurance (extra work!) that what they were doing was OK. I guess we all believe what we want to believe.

There are crossovers in how clients see sex workers, and how SWERFs see us. Both have this blind spot that allows them to discount anything which doesn't match the fantasy they've created. And certain SWERFs have built entire careers on their views; backtracking would take more guts and integrity than they could dream of. When *The Service* came out, this pro-criminalisation lobby group, Nordic Model Now, wrote a hit piece about me, accusing me of lying about sex work. That lack of self-awareness was wild and also utterly predictable. Imagine deciding that, despite never having set foot in an industry, you're better equipped to critique it than someone who has been there, on and off, her whole adult life.

I wanted to talk more about that crossover because it's something we've both explored in our writing. 'Mother' focuses a lot on Mumsnet and most of the quotes about prostitution are lifted straight from that site. My friend Molly Smith wrote a piece about how indistinguishable the language about sex work is on Mumsnet and on the most violent client forums. It speaks to their pornographic interest in it all. When Sussex University produced some resources for student sex workers there was a SWERF response which included the claim that lots of sex workers lose their voices from doing too much deep-throat. It's such a strange and specific fantasy, but they're obsessed with it! They accused my publisher of having blood on their hands because I have a deep throat scene in my book. It's funny on one level and maybe we should take it as a compliment that they think we're all these deep throat queens!

Their obsessions with trans women and with sex workers are so lurid and dramatic, very moral panic-y (very gothic!). The threat they believe we represent is always sexualised. Their arguments are never around how people can make enough money to live, or migrate safely, or have access to healthcare, never about a world completely changed. Their outrage is so selective. Critiquing the violence that happens in sex work without talking about sexual violence in other industries, or without looking at the parallels with hetero-sexual marriage, is so suspect.

I'm thinking about Angela Davis on the racist, patriarchal origins of legislation meant to protect women and children.

SWERFs' belief that you can criminalise your way to safety has not worked in the VAWG movement, and it won't work with prostitution. But this belief in protecting a specific type of women (what Alison Phipps would call the 'cultural power of victimised white womanhood) is so strong.

So, yeah, trying to get inside a SWERF headspace in *The Service* was interesting and took a lot of work. The first version I wrote of Paula, she was just a walking set of bad opinions. I had to add a lot to her character and, weirdly, she probably became the most fleshed out. I still wouldn't be mates with her though!

How do you feel about TERFs almost pornographic fascination? And then I'd like to ask about what you said at the end: that there could have been these shared goals with TERFs; that buried deep down there are some mutual understandings about gender. Do you have any thoughts about where it all went wrong and do you have any hope for the future?

ALISON:

Hi Frankie, I've already told you, perhaps drunkenly, that I think your novel *The Service* is in fact Gothic, especially in relation to the second half where the action begins to culminate in a Church in central London. In that way I believe there is more in common with our books than just a similarity with how we try to talk about these hateful bigots. If *The Service* is a Gothic novel (I know you probably don't agree with me on this but bear with me) then we both had the impulse to write about whatever world we are in (Modernity? Postmodernity? Postpostmodernity? The contemporary?) through the venue of the Gothic. The modern world is a rotting in a very similar way to the classic castles of Gothic tradition. Not in a *moral degradation is rot* way – I already said I've been worrying about accidentally inhabiting a reactionary mindset. I do always find it funny the way my personal life relates to Gothicism – after all, the sink-puke-Virgin Mary experience seems so ridiculously over the top to count as part of that aesthetic. I've spent the last few years living in a variety of decaying, mouldy flats. At one point I was literally lodging in a tiny room in someone else's house like the madwoman in the attic, and at that point my mental health was bad enough that I practically was.

I think it's understandable that you would, in some way, feel embittered (is this the correct word?) by your experiences as a sex worker. I don't know what Alison in 20 years would think about what I'm writing now. I know that because my work is so concerned with the contemporary, so I imagine I'll probably think I'm quite cringe. But me now will also probably think Alison in 20 years' time was cringe too, so that's probably okay. My guess is that I probably move politically further left, which has been my current steady trend over the past decade or so. If that's not the case then I suppose I hope we invent time travel very soon so I can go to the future and kick my own arse.

I'm sorry to hear about your breasts – what a normal

thing to write, well done Alison. If you want, perhaps you could hold a small funeral or memorial service for them. 27 years… is definitely longer than I've been alive, so it's really quite impressive to consider. I hope that removing them helps you! I've been self-administering hormones recently and my body has been changing in interesting, small ways. My sex drive has dropped, although it comes back in strange, unpredictable ways. I've been debating with my partner about whether I've begun developing breasts – she thinks I have, I don't agree, I feel like she probably knows my body better than I do though. I guess this relates to idea of Alison in 20 years – it's really hard to even conceive of what me two decades from now even lives like! I've always struggled conceptualising a future for myself. For a while I just assumed I'd be dead by now, and I'm not, which can be quite confusing. If you could meet the Frankie from 20 years ago, do you think you would be able to have a productive conversation? What would she say to you, and what would you say to her?

The way SWERFs talk about sex worker's bodies has obvious similarities to the ways TERFs talk about trans bodies, as well as the ways clients and chasers also talk about them. There's an obsession with ideas of mutilation happening to us, that once we do something, it *irreversibly damages* us and takes us away from the (white/cis/abled) ideal. A lot of the way this manifests is through creepy obsessions with young girl's bodies being pure, and that transitioning or engaging in sex work destroys this purity – it's one of the many, many ways that TWERF/SWERF thinking basically aligns with full white supremacist, hardcore misogynist belief. Andrea Dworkin, still often so beloved amongst academic feminist circles, characterises images such as a sex worker giving oral sex as being corrupting and sickening. Dworkin was a radical feminist and famously not a TERF no matter what some modern ones think. She was a radical feminist in the proper sense – she did not uphold sex as a biological category and believed that being a woman was something that happened to one. If modern 'radfems' had half of her analysis we might be in a better place, but Dworkin's influence was always going to lead, I think, to where we are now, because she lacked class consciousness. She might not have been personally transphobic but the way she talked about bodies gave fuel to the people who were. I have to be vague about this but we know that certain famous TERFs and transphobes have previously engaged in sexual behaviour with trans people. I've heard many stories about direct messages, about wandering hands. I've also heard stories about famous comedians who publicly deride trans woman and yet are frequent, well-paying and on the whole very polite clients to trans street sex workers in LA. The Chaser is a spector in the trans community that is often talked about but not really understood; people will call any person with a sexual interest in trans people a chaser, which I don't agree with. But people will also somehow forgive obvious chasers just because they say they respect us!

Obviously chasers are very often clients of trans sex workers as well. But there are clients who fetishize the simple fact that someone is a sex worker. Do you think this is a symptom of the way these people talk about bodies?

FRANKIE:

Hmm, so most of the clients I have these days want to believe that our relationship isn't just transactional. They're desperate to escape the reality that I'm a hooker and they're buying my sexual consent and buying my attention. The intense girlfriend experience that lots of us offer these days relies on selling this deep-fake authenticity and clients want that!

In some ways, it's similar to what SWERFs want: that people only have sex out of *authentic desire*. The alternative is intolerable for both of them. Clients for their own egos, SWERFs because they believe having sex without enthusiastic consent is intrinsically damaging. In one way, both of these viewpoints are products of capitalism; the belief that some things (specifically any feminised form of labour) are too special to be commodified. I think most of us would be horrified at the thought of a nanny who hated children but, if they were doing a good job, would it matter? In these spheres, where we believe something should be done only for love, we can't bear the thought of the inauthentic.

So in terms of charging for something that capitalist society tells us should be done for free, I get people's argument that sex work complicates patriachal power relations. But needing money for rent and needing an orgasm are not commensurate, so nothing important about the power relation is changed and in my mind there is nothing radically subversive about the sex industry. It's bullshit to pretend the industy isn't massively gendered and I can't count how many heterosexual marriages I must have propped up by providing an easy, safe outlet for bored cishet men. Where the SWERFs are ridiculous is blaming sex workers for this. Like, on the one hand we're all victims, on the other, we have this huge responsibility to single-handedly overturn patriarchy by becoming homeless.

It's legit to feel like the overriding of bodily boundaries which happens in sex work is unique, but it doesn't mean it's uniquely *bad*. During the six years I was a waitress/bartender in my late 20s, I also felt broken by some work-places, just in a different way.

I love the idea that *The Service* is a gothic novel! I didn't write it from a place of being informed about literary tradition at all but since then I've started thinking more seri-ously about writing, and books. The novel I'm working on now, which is looking at chronic illness (woo! fun!), perhaps has more gothic elements. Despite taking this gamble on taking out my implants, I'm also aware that trauma can live in the body as chronic pain, and the idea of illness as an expression of what was unspeakable fits really well with ideas of monstrosity and Gothicism.

I was thinking about you living in an attic and feeling like a madwoman. When I started doing sex work, I'd just turned 18 and I was living in Amsterdam with my friend. We lived in this attic bedsit and I remember the sink was perma-nently blocked with this dark green water, and covered in flies. (Another sink! Another attic! Another madwoman!) It was summer and really hot. We were sharing a bed and, for a few weeks, we both got sleep paralysis; we'd have to take turns sleeping/waking each other up because it literally felt like we were being possessed by demons. The agency sex work I was doing back then wouldn't start until late at night, and then my pager would go off. I'd have to run down the stairs to the payphone across the street! The rest of the time, we just wanted to take drugs but we didn't want people to know we were smoking crack – it was frowned on! – so we'd go to daytime happy hours and do coke with these older guys who'd pay for everything, and that was what looking like you had your shit together involved back then! So that's the Frankie who I look back on and feel quite protective of, and also kind of impressed by. I was so fearless and now I'm like this anxious fucking mouse. I can't even imagine trying to have a conversation with that version of myself. She'd tell me to fuck off to be honest.

I hate that you struggle to imagine a future for yourself. The world should not be like this. Though to some extent, I think it's always impossible to see yourself as old, or even older. I'm looking forward to reading whatever you write in your 40s! God, 20 years down the line for me is mid-60s and I doubt I'll still be able to string a sentence together. My brain is so addled with painkillers and benzos at the moment I feel myself becoming senile way ahead of time.

I'm thinking about the way SWERFs and TERFs talk about our bodies. I keep worrying that I'm not crediting people properly, but I'm thinking here about pieces I've read by Amrou Al-Kadhi, Arya Karijo and Sophie Lewis that link English transphobia to colonialism and the obsession with 'biological reality' as a basis for excluding this monstrous (and sexually predatory) 'other'. That arrogance that allows you to name something you have no experience of, and to walk over someone's lived experience, feels deeply imperialist and absolutely applies to both SWERFs and TERFs.

Like you said, the crossover with blatant fascism is more obvious even than that. In France, SWERFs are often the same people who campaign against the veil. Remember those images of a Muslim woman being stripped of her veil on a beach? It reminds me of the sex workers who were dragged onto the street in Soho and photographed by the *Evening Standard* during a big sweep of brothel raids in 2013. And that sort of Islamophobia definitely has resemblances to TERFism in its belief that innocents are being radicalised. Mumsnet rants about 'rapid onset gender dysphoria' come from this place of fear and hatred that definitely has similarities to discourse around Muslim radicalisation.

In the US, anti-sex work campaigners are often Christian fundamentalists so there's a big crossover with anti-abortion rhetoric. In the UK, a lot of the first anti-prostitution campaigners in the late 1800s were also heavily involved in the anti-vivisection movement. I remember in the 90s you'd see a lot of really graphic animal rights imagery – dismembered rabbits and torn apart foxes – and it's very reminiscent of anti-abortion images, bloody foetuses and forceps etc. I'm sure if they could get away with it, SWERFs would bombard us of images of sex workers' bodies but they have to make do with words.

And of course, this drawing parallels feels like a very white thing to be doing, when there is no much direct racism in the way sex work is policed and legislated. Anti-trafficking policy is time and time again used to prop up deportations and the solidifying of borders. Even before Brexit, I'd heard about Eastern European women being deported for doing sex work, because it wasn't seen as real work necessary to fulfil migration rules. And then in the US, the horror of that Walking While Trans bill that activists got overturned, showed up the way anti-prostitution sentiment is racist and transphobic at its heart.

I wanted to go back to something you said earlier, about not wanting to read dystopias that involve gender. I'd love to hear more about that, and about what you would like to read more of.

Also, you include an excerpt from Isabel Fall's 'I Sexually Identify as an Attack Helicopter' at the front of *Tell Me I'm Worthless* and I was wondering how you felt about that whole showdown? I'd left Twitter by then but I get this wave of panic when I think about what happened and imagine what it would feel like if part of the online sex work community lost their shit over something I'd written. Is that something you worried about?

ALISON:

Okay, so I may have been a speaking out of turn when I said

that about gendered dystopias, given that in a way… I am writing one. In *Brainwyrms*, there are sequences set in a near future UK where, essentially, the GCs won – transness is not just being morally mandated out of existence but people are forcibly detransitioned by the state. It's basically just trying to work out every worst-case scenario I can think of. So yes, I'm a fucking awful hypocrite but I do stand by the thrust of what I said, which is that I think cis imaginaries about what a gender dystopia are seem to be flawed and useless at best and actively offensive (see the whole Sandra Newman mess) at worst. Too many of them simply read as rewrites of *The Handmaid's Tale* with new wrinkles; and *The Handmaid's Tale* didn't even work as a text when it came out as an analysis of misogyny.

One thing I'd like to ask you about is how you feel about a thing we both do and which we've sort of skirted around here. The two of us both write fiction which takes into account political issues. We have specific political and social outlooks which we want to get across in our fiction. With *Tell Me I'm Worthless* I wanted to explore the relationships between TERFs and transness and how people's experiences and traumas are exploited by the right-wing. *Brainwyrms* is (I think) about the ways in which the British media pushes fascist ideas and suppresses left-wing ideas in pursuit of balance, as well as right-wing hypocrisy and fearmongering about the exploitation of kids, and the particular derangement that Twitter, Facebook and Mumsnet seem to have brought on to the 'British Brain' (it's still work in progress which is why I'm not really sure yet haha).

You know I have been worrying once again about what happened to Isabel Fall, just because this book is more extreme than *Tell Me I'm Worthless* in terms of content, and the tone of the novel is very different. It's told at a remove and is satirical. So I have been worried that it could happen to me, which I know a lot of trans people are, even if the specifics of what happened to Fall were very unique to the situation, and make it all the more upsetting. I think a lot of the discourse around her, though, fails to take into account her voice and opinions, as difficult as that can be, given that she's not public. Have you read the story? It really is a remarkable piece of writing.

I think basically what we're finding through this conversation is something we obviously already knew but which we are crystalising here; these individual bigotries are part of a larger whole, an international network of organisations and individuals which are all interconnected. One thing I notice when TERFs hear us say this about them is that it's ridiculous because they're just, say, a single mum, one journalist etc which is a very silly misunderstanding of how it happens – we don't think each individual TERF is receiving nice checks from some group called the Christian Family Foundation or whatever. We don't think every SWERF is having nice cars bought for them by Exodus Cry. The way these groups fund and move money and resources around is far more complicated than that. It isn't a secret cabal of sinister people, which is, you know, a reactionary idea anyway. But the intense islamophobic ideology of France is intertwined with, say, Rowling, or Don't Say

Gay. It's not *follow the money*. It's about following the lines of ideological belief. It was easy for me to imagine some great evil in this country, a haunted house that contains the sum of Britain's evil. In my new book I have a similar idea but one I'm trying to make sure is more complicated, less easy to sum up in one sentence. What do we do, though, when faced with what is essentially an international movement to the right that is targeting people like us specifically? Well I guess what we ourselves are doing is trying to unpick their ideas from within. Reaching in and pulling at the loose threads 'til they come apart. But can writing fiction do anything beyond that? Do you have any hopes about what our work specifically can achieve?

FRANKIE:

Ugh. The disingenuousness of TERFs (and SWERFs) refusing that their ideology is part of a wider spread of fascism, and their insistence that they're 'just a journalist' or 'just a single mum', and that they represent some sort of authentic working class voice, is very hard to take. I've read so many pro-criminalisation reports into prostitution that literally do not mention austerity, or that quote cops as experts. And then you've got Women's Place UK etc obsessing with changing rooms, with zero analysis of poverty. All of this fearmongering is straight from the right-wing playbook.

It's very easy to be completely overwhelmed by

everything that's going on; to be, on one hand, filled with fear about the future, and on the other riddled with guilt about relative privilege in a world where people are being bombed in their houses and drowning in boats trying to cross the Channel. I'm not doing much activism at the moment because I don't have the capacity but yes, writing for me has been impossible to separate from the need to try and make a political point.

I do think fiction can change the way people think. Though I wonder what it takes for someone to read something and start seeing humanity in a person they've always seen as *other*, when fiction is ultimately read as entertainment and part of its pleasure is voyeurism. I've thought a lot about how fiction can help you see yourself, particularly as a sex worker, when sex workers are so over-represented as fictional subjects and so under-represented as authors. Michelle Tea' *Rent Girl* will always and forever be my favourite description of being a sex worker, I remember when I first read it and it just rang so true. Also Kai Cheng Thom's *Fierce Femmes and Notorious Liars* opened my mind to how you can write about pain in a way that's also warm and beautiful. I love them!

I did read Fall's story and I agree that it's breathtaking. What happened to her is so hard because of course no one should be forced to out themselves. But then I've definitely been pissed off by depictions of sex workers in fiction that are, I assume, written by non-sex workers. It's not that I think people can only write about themselves but there's definitely a level of deep-diving that I don't think anyone should do around a marginality that isn't their own.

But we need to unpick the pressure to share trauma as a way of legitimising yourself, and that pressure comes from all sides. I was thinking about the difference between centring people with marginalisations in political movements – which is how it should be – and fetishizing marginality so that people's validity starts to be intertwined with having a shit time. Both SWERFs and TERFs have really wedded particular identities to suffering and find it unbearable when anyone has a different relationship to gender or sex. But we do that on the Left too – I've been guilty of it – and while I really welcomed the pushback against the 'happy hooker' trope, I do think there needs to be space for joy, in activism and in fiction. (I'm just unlikely to be the person who writes it, in relation to sex work! God help me). What do you think?

ALISON:

I am enjoying the sun today, drinking a cold brew in a cafe that used to be a shop called Cyberdog which sold rave/ fetish wear. Brighton now is already a very different place than it was when I moved here. I know from reading widely that the Brighton I've experienced is not close to what it once was – there used to be a transvestite bar on London Road, and a Dyke Bar where the Sainsbury's now is. A lot of middle to upper class journalists present themselves as essentially the conduits of a kind of silenced majority of women. But is, say, Sarah Ditum, a very rich woman who said she kept her maid coming in through lockdown, *really* a *woman* or a *mum* in the same way as your average working-class mum? Maybe Ditum is not the best example. If we think about JKR, though, she is a person who was once a single mum, but whom an impossible amount of wealth and power has made, I think, socially distinct from the categories of *woman* and *mother* that she may once have occupied. This is a wild claim perhaps, which is why I'm nesting it so deep in this conversation. I'm not saying she isn't a woman or a mum, but that wealth and class position must surely alienate someone from the reality of those categories. JKR bought her children huge tree houses to live in, for Christs' sake. I think the ability to do that means you functionally don't have anything at all in common with a woman who can barely afford to buy her kids a Christmas present. You are a woman still, you are a mother but you are not a woman and a mother. Does any of this make sense?

I do try to present happiness and joy in relation to queerness. It's hard because, you know, I'm a horror writer, so I want to write horrible things. But I worry I'm presenting purely misery, which isn't my experience. So joy creeps in around the edges, especially in relation to personal connection and sex. Even as sex is sometimes bleak and nasty in my work, it also provides a space for connection between individuals, however fleeting. I don't want to demonise queer sex given that I love having it! *Tell Me I'm Worthless* I think discloses too much of my own personal traumas so I'm moving back from that with *Brainwyrms*, which is anyway less about trauma and more about things that are happening and going to happen. It's a dystopia. I quit poetry because I couldn't stop dwelling on my trauma and forcing it into some grand narrative, which wasn't really accurate to how it even happened. Things happened to me, randomly, pointlessly. It didn't mean that I was being pushed towards spiritual transcendence, that I was medusa or an angel. I got too full of myself. People didn't need to know everything that ever happened to me. I'm an artist. My audience is not my therapist. So yes I guess even if I, a horror writer, do include suffering in my work, I am trying to pull away from tying myself to that because it doesn't help anyone to wallow in the pain – trans people and sex workers still deserve respect even if they haven't ever experienced anything traumatic. How do we go about rethinking this though? And are we losing something from doing it?

At the same time, it would, I think, be offensive of me to erase all forms of trauma and violence from relation to queer life. I think it's perfectly fine for there to be media such as, say, *Heartstopper*, which tells a queer story which is relatively without conflict. After all, that's a piece of media aimed at young adults. Most media aimed at young adults is comparatively devoid of real life violence. But I have also seen comparisons between that show and other pieces of media that essentially demonise other queer art for depicting more complex realities. Of course, being queer does mean, on a basic level, that you are more vulnerable to violence, and sanitising art from reflecting that is tantamount to whitewashing it I think.

FRANKIE:

I'm glad you're outside in the sun! I'm now one week away from finishing sex work and I'm genuinely excited about having to take some time off to recover from surgery and then, hopefully, to be in loads better health and able to start my new life, whatever that might be! I don't know what I'm going to do next but I feel strangely hopeful.

So, yeah, writing joy. I've had a rule for a long time that I don't want to read or watch anything which leaves me feeling terrible unless it's such exquisite art it's worth the pain. Life is hard enough. *Tell Me I'm Worthless* passed the test, but with *The Service*, which is definitely not a literary masterpiece, it felt important to leave people with resolution and warmth. I've found so much love and solidarity in the sex work community, and despite being terrible at sexual romance, I'm good at friendships – which are anyway, in their way, romantic – and I've always had really strong networks of friends, so I wanted to write about that. On the other hand, I feel completely okay about using fiction to work through your own shit and I don't subscribe to the belief that you need to have healed from something before you can write about it. Write from that bleeding wound! It's okay!

And I absolutely agree about not erasing trauma or feeling some obligation to always present art that contains resolution. I'm also thinking about the specific ways women are supposed to experience pain. After the violent rape scene in Virginie Despentes' *Basie Moi*, one of the characters is disgusted with Manu because she doesn't cry and is too passive. That scene really stayed with me because I've had other women tell me I must be in denial about specific incidents of violence when I haven't reacted in the *right* way.

How we begin unpicking the Left's worshipping of trauma and suffering, I'm not sure. We need to examine the belief that marginality equals moral superiority. Kai Cheng Thom talks about how, in Left organising spaces, privilege is basically seen as original sin. I think this thinking is also what causes these huge gaps in thinking – the way the #MeToo movement was overtaken by whiteness and then women's pain at having that critiqued. We need to remember we can all be victims *and* perpetrators; being marginalised in one way doesn't mean you can't also cause harm.

Going back to what you said, that you're not being pushed towards spiritual transcendence, like an angel, by pain – I'd love to hear more of your thoughts about that. There's this whole self-help culture that really feeds into this belief, isn't there? As if personal *manifestation* stands a fighting chance against structural inequality.

God, it's such a sunny, lovely day and it feels wrong to bring the conversation back to bleakness. Back to joy! (We've also just decided that these will be our final responses – this chat could carry on and on but it's only ever a drop in the ocean of the wider conversation. I keep reminding myself that to help with the anxiety!)

I was trying to think of things I'll miss about sex work, apart from the money, and it's the camaraderie. I had a long booking in a dungeon this week with a friend who I work with a lot and, at this point, we know each other so well it's like we have one hooker brain! All service industries involve parallel experiences for the worker and the person buying that service, but it's so magnified in sex work. And experiencing that from the inside, as well as being part of a community that's so stigmatised, can lead to these really magical, synchy connections. Anyway this session was particularly funny and psychic and I will genuinely miss those sort of moments with other hookers.

So I guess I'll end with that – love and solidarity to all the whores, even the ones who think I should be buried alive for being so grumpy about hooking! Shout out to the English Collective of Prostitutes (ECP), SWARM and Decrim Now. And solidarity to you, Alison. Can't wait to read your next book! x

ALISON:

I was helping a friend move house today. It was tough because of how warm it was; at every point I wanted to give up and just go sit in a pub garden somewhere. It was worth it because, frankly, I like feeling useful. I've had to move on my own before and it's a gruelling, depressing task. Once we were done, we sat in their garden and drank wine. I talked with another friend who joined us about politics and also about writing. The other friend lived for some time in Nicaragua, and has been very distressed by the political situation there over the last few years. She told me that even if it's bad here, and getting worse, she feels safer here, and she feels guilty for that. Safety of course is… relative; one person's *I feel safe* is another person's *I do not feel safe*, even if, in fact, both individuals are the same *amount* of safe.

I'm glad you feel hopeful for the future! Hope is a rare, difficult thing, and having it is wonderful. Holding onto it though… that's the task, isn't it? I hope you can do it. I hope we both can!

You should stop talking down *The Service*, however, which is a wonderful, smart, humane book that I think will be recognised for just how great it is. However, moving past that… I do engage quite a lot in, frankly, miserable art. It's part of what comes with being a fan of extreme cinema, which is often, at its base, nasty and disgusting, and at its worse it can feel actively exploitative – they don't call it exploitation for nothing! I expose myself to a lot of stuff that makes me feel like *shit*, to put it simply. I respect that you don't; I'm not strong enough because in a way I almost crave the shitty feeling of sudden transphobia in an old horror film, or something similar.

I think it was in a way selfish that I became so convinced that my pain was transcendent. It's a very self-centred view… it helped for me to remember that I am just part of a network of organisms, and am no more important than anyone else. I suppose what I was experiencing may well have been close to Catholic thinking about suffering or sin. Self-help does this too, and Scientology, but Catholicism was closer to what I was doing because I was putting myself at the center of a grand narrative that was almost epic in scope and scale.

We are not God's pawns, or punching bags. And the pain we have experienced is simply pain. It is sometimes people's fault, it sometimes isn't. There are people who have also experienced pain, and experiencing that puts them in a similar position to us, so we should find them, and we should tell them they aren't alone, and then we should make sure no one else is hurt. This is simple and moralistic in a way, but you know. It's hopeful. I don't have a huge amount of hope in general right now, but I avoid being a doomer, which is a shockingly unhelpful way of being. I think if I want someone to get something from this it would be that conversations which are always ongoing and developing are one of the oldest ways we have of forming solidarity and developing community strength. So solidarity to you, to them, to us and to the reader – let's keep talking. Let's bite the Queen.

AUTHOR'S NOTE

Following is an interview with Natalia Santana Mendes, a trans sex worker from Brazil whose story, different from either of ours but also familiar, could be told by her alone. Natalia died in March 2021. Neither of us met her but she was part of our community, in a wider sense and literally. Natalia spent almost two decades visiting the UK to work and was a member of the English Collective of Prostitutes (ECP).

This book was always deeply personal; a conversation about how we feel living these lives, in these bodies, in this place and time. And to this, from another continent and another life, Natalia's story is a reminder of the world's wild variation, of disparate levels of privilege and access to resources, and of the loves, and fears, and anger that tie us together.

Natalia experienced incredible hardship and violence and she was clear-sighted about the structures which enable this: the fascist governments, the brutal policing, the closed borders, the transphobia, the misogyny, the racism, and the role of every SWERF and TERF and bigot whose tacit support props up the whole fucking thing. It's inspiring that, despite everything, Natalia was so humorous and full of joy and energy for change.

It is an honour to include Natalia's voice in this book.

Frankie & Alison

This interview transcription was taken from a collection of recordings that have yet to be published. We're printing it here with the permission of Heston Michaels (English Collective of Prostitutes) and Marina Oliveira Santos.

When you introduce yourself, you use the term 'travesti' as well as transsexual and I noticed your tattoo 'Furia Travesti' – can you say what the meaning and significance of this is? As well as the reason you choose to describe yourself as a 'puta' rather than sex worker?

I am identifying with both transsexual and travesti. Travesti, this is an identity for us in Brazil, and across many countries in South America also. A travesti, she is assigned male from birth, and then to belong to the feminine gender like the transsexual and the cisgender woman, but she is not to necessarily see herself to be a woman, though some of us do. For me, it is political. I use it for this reason and to honour the culture of trans women and travesti I was raised from. The word, it has a stigma and a legacy of criminalisation, of poverty, of prostitution. To use it is important as resistance to this and the colonialism that has enforced the binary sex and gender. Furia Travesti (Travesti Fury), this is our united battle cry, we are furious. It is representing our struggle, our resilience, our resistance, and our freedom.

Puta (Whore), to me, I am using this for similar reason, it is political. You will see my necklace; it says this word. It is part of our struggle against stigma and as a refusal also to be seen as a victim. It is not because I am happy to be doing this work, but I am not ashamed of what I have done to survive and provide for my family. Gabriela Leite, a mother of the Brazilian sex worker movement who has passed in 2013, she said, "sons of putas" is one of the most offensive things you can call someone in Brazil, and we must change this. "Sons of putas", this should be a name of pride for our children". This resonates with me. But society would prefer we starve on the streets than to become whores. So, I use it for this reason, but I use sex worker also.

I'd like to talk about your current family, but can you first briefly tell us about your upbringing. You transitioned when you were very young. What was that like and how did you discover that was a possibility for you?

I was raised in the 1980s in the north zone of Rio de Janeiro by my mother. For many years, she is raising me and my four brothers alone, I have no memory of my father. My mother, she had endured many years of beatings from him and she leaves him soon after I was born. It was a difficult life, she worked very hard to support us, but we were very poor and there is a lot of violence where we are living. There is many problems with the police. My mother, she is married once more when I am seven. The man who is to become my new father, he is kinder to her, but he is very abusive and violent to me for my feminine appearance and behaviours. It is a very strict Catholic home, very conservative and he is to say he is disgusted by the way I walk and talk. My mother, she was ashamed of me also. I am knowing from a young age that I am not a boy, it is very hard to explain this feeling. When I am discovered to be living as a girl I am thrown to the streets and am having to find a way to survive. This is the story for most of us, our lives as women start and end on the street.

How old were you at this point?

I am 12 when it is discovered. Most of us, we are taking on this identity at this age. I already have been on the street, many nights to not be at home many times, to escape this abuse. But when I am to be discarded, it was a very desperate and traumatic experience. Many people they are to take advantage of this situation and you must do things that affect you very deeply. There is no choice but to become a prostitute, this is a sacrifice we make to live this life. You are to escape violence and abuse only to face more of this, but there is the freedom and the dream that you will now be able to change yourself, and it is this belief which is to keep you in this life.

There are many of us on the street, travesti are very visible. Others, they are with the same story. It is Carmella who is to become my mother figure. It is from her and the other women I learn how to survive and become a woman. We lived many of us together, it was not easy, many of the girls they are traumatised, many of us, we are taking many drugs to escape this life. But we soon are to learn that all we have is each other and we are to depend on this family to survive.

Have you seen your parents or your brothers since you were thrown out?

So, it has been 25 years since this time. My brothers I am seeing sometime in the beginning years, but all have passed now. My mother and father, they are alive. I have been home two times. One time I return with much defiance and very dramatic when I am 17 to scream that I have now got tits and am a beauty queen (laughs). The next time, this is many years later in a more "dignified" way (laughs) in hope that time perhaps has healed the wounds. But it has not. I fear it will never be in this lifetime. I am sending money home every month to my mother, to show I can provide, to perhaps prove that I am worthy, deserving of something. I do not know. We do not speak but I hope she is thinking something good of me. I think we are all wanting our mothers to love us.

You have your own child now, right?

Yes, my son, who is now not small, (laughs), he is 20. I know I am looking too young for this to be true! (laughs). He is everything to me and I am very proud of him. I have raised him for many years alone but his father who has given birth to him, he is in his life in the recent years. It was very difficult at first, I am worried for what he would face because of who his mother is. Also, at this time, it is when he is age one that I am tested positive for HIV. There was some time of very bad health, of much sadness and fear.

I always am speaking of being a mother, of raising my son, and raising the young travesti also whose birth mothers have discarded them. It is important as it is hard work, and it is not seen as having value. The role of the mothers, this is not respected by society, and this must change. Most of us we are not just trying to survive ourselves, we are having many others depending on us, and to have this, to have many to provide for, you are having always to make much more money. It is more of a worry and a pressure; you do not want to see those you love suffering. You are hoping you can give to them something to make life a little easier. To be looked at with love. To not feel they are in this world alone. You do what you can you know?

Can you provide a picture of what it can be like to be a trans sex worker in Brazil?

It is not an exaggeration to say that it is a state of emergency for travesti in Brazil. 90% of us, we are ending up on the streets very young and are surviving through prostitution. Many of us, we have been sex workers all our lives. No one will give us employment. We are told if you are to be a travesti you are to be a prostitute, you are to be poor, to be ridiculed and dehumanised. We are in a cycle of poverty and violence. For many, it is a struggle every day for even many of the basic things, to eat, to not be attacked. The life expectancy for a trans women is 35, and it is 75 for the average population. This, it should show what we are facing.

The violence is very bad. They are killing us one by one; it is a social cleansing. You ask any of the girls out there on the street what is happening, and they will tell you of the attacks, the rapes, the murders. The killings, many, they are enacted with much cruelty, with torture, mutilation. Many girls they are also getting shot, stabbed, run down in public spaces. This is from the police and militia also, they terrorise us, and this, it is allowed to continue because no one cares about another dead travesti. We are dehumanised even in death where they are to say we are "men dressed as women" and blamed for what has happened to us. Many cannot endure this suffering. We do not say we are committing suicide; we say we are being killed by suicide. It is still murder by the state. We are mourning and demanding justice for our sisters, but where are the mass protests for us?

Our community has been abandoned; we do not have access to most of society. There is a stigma that surrounds us, that we are crazy, and aggressive, that we are exaggerated and flamboyant, that we are attracting violence. And there is the view we are all prostitutes, addicted to substances and have HIV, which means they are viewing us also as deviants, as something immoral, carriers of disease. Around 30% of the girls, they do have HIV which carries much stigma, this is 55 times higher than the average population in Brazil. There is a lot of prejudice, and this, it makes it difficult to access many places, to get healthcare, to get any support we are needing. Many girls, they have died from health complications, including AIDS complications, things that could be treated because of the fear of going to a hospital or because they were turned away or they have left because they were treated very badly. And when you are not able to get the transition treatments, of course this is forcing many of us to risk our health with other methods to change our bodies.

Has anything changed in terms of legal rights? Has life improved as a result of this and greater visibility?

There have been many victories. To get sex reassignment surgery through the public health system is an example of this, and to not have to have the surgeries to change the official identity documents. We must celebrate that these things are now possible for the people who are wanting and needing this, but for many girls, there are still many difficulties to access these things, and these things, they are still controlled by the state.

Also, to have rights and legal protections, these, they are not a solution to what is happening to us. We have won some rights on paper, but we are still being killed in the streets. Violence and poverty, these things are increasing. We cannot depend on these legal rights for safety, or for our freedoms. It is not to liberate us to gain rights in this system that is existing, when it is this system that is making and maintaining the oppression of our trans bodies, and racism and many things.

Life, it has improved for some and some, they have a space to speak now, but visibility, this, does not bring protection. It is taking time for the society to change, and when they are seeing you are gaining some grounds, it is those of us who are visible in the street, the sex workers, the poor, the Black and Pardo communities where we are heavily policed, this is who is feeling this backlash. So we cannot think because there is a trans person on a TV or a trans person that has written a book that we have achieved some respect and safety as a community.

Do you think the increase in violence and hostility is linked to the 2018 election of Jair Bolsonaro?

His election has impacted us greatly and since this, murders of trans women, this, it has increased by 45%, with Black trans women being two-thirds of victims. So many, we are feeling this is a direct result of what he represents. But the racial and gender violence, this, it started long ago, it is historical, it does not start here with Bolsonaro. We have always been terrorised; this is nothing new to us, to have to defend our right to exist.

There is much hope for change. There is a stir, we are seeing the Vidas Negras Importam (Black Lives Matter) grow stronger, the fight against sexual violence, the reproductive justice, these, they are gaining more ground, and we are seeing ourselves in these movements now. We have lost our dear Marielle Franco, a strong champion for many of us, but her spirit lives on in us all and many more will rise.

We have seen the first election of an indigenous woman to Brazilian Congress. We have the first trans women to earn positions in state legislature, both Afro-Brazilian trans women. Erika Hilton, she says she is occupying the Brazilian government on behalf of every Black and trans person in Brazil. The state of Bahia, it has elected the first Black woman as its representative. I believe we can win, we will defeat this powers against us if we are uniting.

You've been migrating to the UK for many years to work, but with the situation in Brazil, had you ever considered seeking refuge here or elsewhere permanently?

There has long been the Travesti Diaspora. Many, they have been leaving for Europe and the US since the 1970s. It is a case of survival and dreams of a better life. Some they are applying for the asylum, but many girls, they are living without the papers which is leaving them very vulnerable to many things. There is more possibility of a "normal" life, but there is still much violence and prejudice wherever we are going. We are still trans and we are still prostitutes and we are also becoming then migrant women, so the stigma and the criminalisation, this remains.

I have considered this many times, to not return. When you are attacked or they are threatening you, or a friend is killed, it is the reminder that death it is always close by.

There are times when I have stayed away for a long time because I am traumatised, or I am very scared. I am age 37 now, I have made this past 35, but you are always thinking when will it be my time you know? I have lost many friends in terrible ways, but I try always to not be paralysed by this fear. Brazil, it is my home, I have built my life there, this is where my family remains. I do not want to be forced away. The government, it owes us for all the suffering it has inflicted on us, and for as much as I can, I will go back and I will keep sending this money so it can improve our lives and resist the poverty they are containing us in.

You say women still face a lot of prejudice and violence in Europe, can you say a bit more about that?

It does not matter the border I am crossing, there is still the transphobia, the racism, the sexism. There is a lot of prejudice. Our conditions, they improve of course otherwise we would not come, but we are still remaining in prostitution, we are still struggling to get the housing and basic things we are needing to live. Many things, they are impossible when you do not have the papers. The clients and the police also, they are bad everywhere, there is still much risk of violence and the prostitution laws and anti-immigrant controls, this is making us an easy target. We are still treated as criminals, still seen as disposable. So, it is not an easy life, we are continuing to be excluded from much of society and there is always this fear of deportation. I am carrying a heavy burden for much of the time as I am making many sacrifices to come, to leave family, to leave friends and to worry always what is happening to them and to be trying to make the money to send back. But for me, this is worth this. I survived many years in Brazil, but I am wanting more than survival, I wish to live, to have freedom, to not struggle, to find love. Many things.

Have you felt the impact of the rise in anti-trans feminist sentiment in the UK in recent years?

We are used to these words from the right-wing and religious conservatives in Brazil and around the world, it is this that has helped Bolsonaro and Trump and others to advance. But here, this is deeply embedded in many areas in the UK, in many movements, in places perhaps I am not to expect. These views, they are not to represent the views of everyday women, but the elitist feminists, they are holding much power and political influence, and the public, it is infected by the lies they are portraying. There is already much prejudice and stigma attached to our lives, and when you do not have respect for a population, this, it is leading to more violence and dehumanisation and a denial of rights. But this is the intention. It is because they are seeing we are coming out of the shadows and that we are uniting and advancing, so this hostile climate, it is the backlash to this.

It is giving permissions to abuse and target us. I have faced more aggressions in the street. I have been spat at and called many things, a "faggot", a "pervert", I have had things thrown at me, men, they are shouting "show us your cock" to try to humiliate you. And you are feeling it, you are feeling you are being seen more, that people are suspicious of you, that they are feeling they have a right to question you, to have their opinion of your life.

It is a scandal that anyone is to indulge this madness. To create us as an image of the enemy, to frame our rights as a conflict to the cisgender woman. These tactics, they have been used against many groups that have no power, and it is a very dangerous and deliberate distraction from the real threats to women. While there are these debates, this scrutiny of trans bodies, women, they are to be made poorer by government policies and get no justice for rape and other violence, migrants and asylum seekers, they are abused and deported, people of colour, they are being terrorised by the police, healthcare is in crisis, the UK government wages war around the world and the planet is burning.

You say there is hostility in places you wouldn't expect, can you expand on that point?

The transphobia, it has a grip on many parts of society. The feminists, you are expecting this of some, they are having no problem to align with the right-wing and religious conservatives to push their agenda, who are to call on more police, more criminalisation, more state powers. They are not interested to fight the systemic problems, they have only an interest in themselves. There has always been this problem, and many women suffer because of this.

But other organisations, some good organisations who do not align with these perspectives, there is deep-rooted transphobia in some spaces also. They do not see these ways they are enforcing the rigid sex and gender binary that is created to benefit those with power, that has criminalised, stigmatised and attempted to eradicate us throughout the history and is the source of their own oppression and struggles also. Instead of to expand their organising to include us, they are seeing us a threat also.

There is much suspicion of us from these spaces, a questioning always, a need for us to defend our experience, to provide the argument against the lies that a right-wing media is spreading, like the view it is perhaps holding some valid questions or some truths. There is an interrogation, a hostility as this starting point, rather than asking how they can include and support you in the struggle. This, it is making it hard to organise with some parts of society when they are viewing us and treating us in this way.

But we unearth this now, it is clear who is with us. We see who is not speaking up in our defence unless the hand is forced, we see who is not providing us a space to speak on our experiences or who is not making reference to our struggles. We see who holds prejudice and has many views on us and our movement and demands without ever speaking to us or knowing anything of our lives. But things, they are changing. Organisations emerging now, movements that are growing, they are coming instant with a trans inclusive mindset. There is no question. They are viewing this as part of their own liberation, they are having an international perspective on gender, they are knowing that transphobia and sexism has the same roots as racism, they are knowing this connection and they fighting to overthrow this colonial legacy that has been inflicted on us.

It doesn't go un-noticed that many of the prominent anti-trans groups and figures are also anti-sex work and are pushing for laws to criminalise sex workers' clients. Can you say about what impact those laws have?

It is the same feminists of course. They are having many opinions on which women are deserving of respect and protections. I do not understand how these laws can be seen to be feminist and to help women. It is very clear this is not the truth. It is a moral crusade with racist police and border control as its army that is making us poorer and more vulnerable to violence. I still must work, it is a cruel act to try to take away an option that we are depending on to survive. They are to give no real alternatives, the exiting programmes, these, they are not fit for purpose. Other jobs, they are worse, there is more exploitation, less pay, and many of us cannot get this other work. This is why we are doing the prostitution! But they are knowing this, they are not interested in tackling the roots, it is easier to put the blame on one place, to try to eradicate this.

Where this law has come to, all of the countries, there has been the same effects on us. More violence, worse conditions, more stigma also. In France there has been more murders of migrant trans women. Sex workers, we are being evicted, charged as "pimps", deported. Mothers, they are having their children taken from them. It is a lie that we are not targeted directly. When there is any criminalisation, it is to bring contact with the police who are sexist, racist and transphobic and we are suffering as a result. This, it is a class issue. They do not let us speak for ourselves, they are seeing us as stupid, that we are not knowing what is best for us, they are to decide what exploitation is acceptable.

The movement for decriminalisation seems to have grown in recent years, especially among younger feminists. What do you think has changed?

It is the same as what we are speaking of with an emergence of our next generation who are to see trans liberation as part of their own struggle. Many are now on our side. Many organisations, they are seeing this now as an issue of human rights, of workers' rights, of safety. Many young people, they are knowing you cannot criminalise people out of poverty. They themselves, they are struggling to survive. We are strengthened by many movements that are making visible the brutality of the police and border control. These issues, they are coming to the surface.

We have many battles ahead, but things, they are changing, and we are uniting, But the sex worker movement, any movement, it must be rooted in the experience of those of us with the least power. It must start from the ground, it cannot be dominated by academics and NGOs and the few who are given a platform, even if they are to be a sex worker, to be trans. It cannot be focused on issues that are to benefit the few, not the many. We must ensure also that criminalisation of prostitution, it cannot be seen as separate, we have a duty to make these connections with others. We are stronger together.

Where do you draw your strength from? Are there any trans and sex worker activists you admire that you'd like people to know about?

I draw strength first from the older women in my life. I know they were terrified and endured so much, but they never let fear prevent them from achieving what was needed. They have survived the dictatorship, the death squads, the start of the AIDS pandemic, many things. We are still experiencing much of what they have faced, but they have raised a new generation of women who are feeling we are now deserving of a better life. They have enabled this, through their love, and through their sacrifices and determination. This work is hidden. It must be made visible, it must be respected by memory. This history, it is always erased, you are to look back and it is like we never existed. We cannot forget them, those that have passed, those that have been imprisoned, those that are now confined to their home as they will no longer survive the dangers outside. They are also still resisting, this is their memory and legacy too, we must keep this alive. They raised us and we owe them a lot.

There are people in our movements I admire, Gabriela Liete, Brenda Lees, Erika Hilton, I look also to others throughout history that have fought slavery, have protected our lands, have protected the Amazon. but no person has changed things alone, this is a collective struggle and the names of many that have led the way for us will never be heard.

There are many others also that have impacted my life, that I do not wish to forget. Silvia, she was a vendor on the street I am working many years ago. She had a small, how do you say it, a shack, a kiosk for many years. She worked long hours for very little, she was in her 60s, a single mother to seven children, four killed in violence, two by the police. She would never be able to rest, to stop working. And she was campaigning also, for justice for her sons. But every day, she would come to us girls, with a smile, with food that she would make for us. She always told me I was beautiful. She always told me to stay strong and that there is nothing wrong with me and what I am. She had the protection of the travestis (laughs) we would drive away anyone that is to try to steal from her or when the police are harassing.

She showed us such kindness, she was the only person who would even look at us as though we are humans. This will stay with me forever. She was a light in the darkness. She has passed away last year sadly. But I think of her every day and pray for her and her family.

I did see you have a lot of religious – what are they, statues, or icons? Who is the saint on your pendant?

Yes, I am very religious, very spiritual, as you are seeing from the alter. This is Pombagira, how to explain this in

English, she is the central female entity in Umbanda and the protector of women, of the sex worker and the travesti. The others here, they are the influence of the Mexican and Colombian girls I have lived with, so La Santa Muerte and other saints, it is their versions of protectors for the trans and the putas. There is a lot of influence, Catholic of course, but Umbanda also, and other Afro-Brazilian religions. It is very important to me, to my identity, and it is to bring comfort and strength. I also find much peace with myself. It will give me the strength to walk through the door, to calm the fear of not returning. For some girls, I do not feel they would be here without this, to not have hope of something more to come, to think this suffering is all there will be and then it is all to end.

Do you have any final closing words of encouragement to those living through these difficult times and the younger generation of trans activists?

It will be difficult and it will be frightening, but we must continue to fight and we will defeat these powers against us. We have no other choice, it is a matter of defending our lives. Change will come from us, as it always had, not from those in power, not from academics, not from the NGOs. We have long been told we do not know how to express ourselves, that we do not know the right words, do not let them speak on your behalf, do not let them tell you that you are not capable. We do not need translators.

We have long shown up for others, we must continue

this, and we must demand they do the same for us. Our liberation, it is entwined with others. We must ensure also we do not forget our elders, the women in prison, the travesti that live by the rivers and in the forests, those who are working on the land, those of us living with illness. Freedom must include us all.

Please continue to dream, and to celebrate. To live your life, to love, to exist. We have much work to do, but part of this is to care for our community, this is a collective respon-sibility, without this we have nothing.

Even the strong, warlike people among us, one day they are to finish their part in this mission and leave us, but their work, their spirits live on. We must hold onto this; we must continue to have hope. We will keep shouting "behind the silicone a heart also beats!". Furia Travesti,

Viva a aliança das mulheres indígenas, negras e trans. (Long live the alliance of indigenous, Black and trans women.) Fica com Deus. (God be with you.) Thank you, Obrigada

Natalia Santana Mendes, 2020

We'd like to mention *CasaNem*, a trans sanctuary house in Rio, one of the organisations that was hugely important to Natalia. You can donate to them here: *https://evoe.cc/casanem*

Frankie Miren is a writer, an occasional journalist and, until halfway through writing this chapbook, a hooker. Frankie's first novel, *The Service* (Influx Press) came out in July 2021. *The Service* is a fictional take on the realities of sex work and swerf-ism in the UK and was informed by twenty-eight years dropping in and out of the industry, in various conditions and on several continents. Frankie is connected to the English Collective of Prostitutes (ECP) and the Sex Workers Advocacy and Resistance Movement (SWARM).

Alison Rumfitt is a writer and semi-professional trans woman. Her debut pamphlet of poetry, *The T(y)ranny*, was a critical deconstruction of Margaret Atwood's work through the lens of a trans woman navigating her own misogynistic dystopia. It was published by Zarf Editions in 2019. *Tell Me I'm Worthless* (Cipher Press, 2021) is her debut novel. Her work has appeared in countless publications such as *SPORAZINE, datableed, The Final Girls, Burning House Press, SOFT CARTEL, Glass Poetry* and more. Her poetry was nominated – twice! – for the Rhysling Award in 2018. You can find her on Twitter @hangsawoman and @alison.zone on Instagram. She loves her friends.